Petey

A radio adaptation of Paul Shipton's story
by David Calcutt

Illustrated by Chris Smedley

Oxford University Pres

Oxford University Press, Great Clarendon Street, Oxford OX2 6DP

Oxford New York
Athens Auckland Bangkok Bogota Buenos Aires Calcutta
Cape Town Chennai Dar es Salaam Delhi Florence Hong Kong
Istanbul Karachi Kuala Lumpur Madrid Melbourne Mexico City
Mumbai Nairobi Paris São Paulo Singapore Taipei Tokyo
Toronto Warsaw

and associated companies in
Berlin Ibadan

Oxford is a trade mark of Oxford University Press

© David Calcutt 1998

First published 1998

Adapted from the novel **Petey** by Paul Shipton,
published by Oxford University Press in 1996.

ISBN 0 19 918796 7

Designed by Holbrook Design Oxford Limited

Printed in Great Britain

Cast list

Sophie

Mum

Dad

Petey

Sam

The voices of the machines: Bus Robot / Traffic Controller / Voice of Advertising Sign / Corrections Squad Robot

Alternatively, the actor playing Mum could also be the voice of the Traffic Controller, while the actor playing Dad could also be the voice of the Advertising Sign.

Introduction

Petey is written as a radio play, which means it's a play to be heard, and not seen. But that doesn't mean there isn't anything to see. It's just that, in this case, the pictures should appear inside the minds of the audience rather than in front of them.

It's like when you listen to a really good story – you can see everything that's happening in the story right there in your mind. And sometimes, this can make it more real than if you were watching it on a screen or a stage. A radio play works like that.

But what can make the play real and bring it to life?

1 *Using your voice*
   In a radio play, the way you use your voice is very important. It's the voices that tell us what's going on, and how the characters are feeling. If you want to make a character sound happy, or fed up, or sad, or excited, you have to use your voice to do it.

2 *Using sound effects*
   To tell the audience what action is happening, or where the action's taking place, you can use sound effects. There's plenty of opportunity in *Petey* for making exciting and unusual sound effects, and you can have a lot of fun doing it.

When you've practised reading the play aloud, and worked out what sound effects are needed, you could try recording part of the play into a tape-recorder, with the sound effects. When you've finished, play it back to see how it sounds. You might even want to try recording the whole play. Then let your class hear it, and see if you can create pictures in their minds.

Petey

The play is set in the future, and opens to the sound of a hover-bus coming to a halt near Sophie's home. The robot driving the bus speaks in a flat voice to Sophie.

Bus-robot   Here you are, Sophie. We have arrived at your home. The time is four twenty-eight precisely.

Sophie   Thanks. But you've dropped me outside the wrong house again!

Bus-robot   I apologize. My destination circuits must be a little worn. I will have to get them fixed.

Sophie   That's what you always say.

Bus-robot   I will see you on Monday morning, Sophie, at eight twenty-six precisely.

6

Sophie	Yes. And try and come to the right house this time.
Bus-robot	Of course. Goodbye.

The hover-bus moves away.
Sophie *narrates.*

Sophie	My name's Sophie Nova. The hover-bus has just brought me home from school – to the wrong house, as usual. And, as I run up to the door of our house, I wonder why it is, if all these robots are supposed to be so efficient, they still make mistakes. But at least our house computer works properly. When I speak to it, it recognizes my voice straight away.

*The **house computer** speaks in a flat voice to Sophie.*

Computer	Good afternoon, Sophie. I am pleased to hear your voice again.
Sophie	Thanks. Can you open the door and let me in, please.

There is a crackling sound.

Computer	Just one moment.
Sophie	What's the matter?

Computer   There appears to be a loose connection. Trying
again.

The door slides open. **Sophie**
enters the house.

The door is now open.

Sophie	Thanks. Did you know, Computer, that people used to have things called keys to open doors for them?
Computer	Keys?
Sophie	Little bits of metal. You stuck them in a hole in the door, and turned them, and the door opened. We learned about them in Ancient History at school today.
Computer	What a primitive idea. We computers are much more efficient.

Sophie narrates.

Sophie	I wonder about that, too, as the door crackles again, then slides shut behind me. All these machines we've got these days, do they really make life any better than it was in the old times? Some of them do, I suppose. But there's one that definitely doesn't. The Ultra-Reality Machine.

*Sophie is in the living room now, and we hear **Mum** and **Dad** speaking aloud, plugged into the Ultra-Reality Machine.*

Mum	Watch out! Enemy starships coming in from the rear!
Dad	Avast there, me hearties! Shiver me timbers!
Sophie	Mum! Dad! I'm home!
Mum	Swing round! Blast them with your laser!
Dad	You scurvy dog! I'll make you walk the plank!

Sophie *narrates.*

Sophie	There they are, as usual, with their helmets on, and both plugged into it. The machine plays a film in the helmet, and it's as if you're in it. It seems like the real world, but it isn't. Me and my brother Sam aren't allowed to go on it, but Mum and Dad are on it all the time. Mum's favourite is the Space Wars programme.
Mum	Got them! Set controls to Warp Speed Factor 9 and let's get out of here!

Sophie	And Dad's is the Pirate programme.
Dad	Yo ho ho, mateys! Set a course for the Spanish Main!

Sophie narrates.

Sophie   I look at them and think how stupid they look, talking to themselves with those daft helmets on. Then I decide I'd be better off going into the kitchen and talking to Petey instead.

We move to the kitchen, where **Petey** *the robot is busy preparing food in the Food Dispenser.*

When **Petey** *speaks, his voice is flat and robotic.*

Petey   Good afternoon. Please wait while I scan my data banks for your name. Ah. There it is. Hello, Sophie.

Sophie   Hello, Petey. What are you up to?

Petey   I am preparing your meal in the Food Dispenser, Sophie. It will be ready for you soon.

Sophie narrates.

Sophie   Petey's our domestic robot – a model PT-3000. That's how he got his name – Petey. He's really old-fashioned and his memory-circuits are slow. Dad was going to get a new one, but then he went and bought that stupid Ultra-Reality Machine instead. I'm glad, though. I like Petey. He's been around for as long as I can remember.

We go back to the kitchen.

Petey Terrible weather we're having, aren't we...
Sophie?

Sophie No, Petey, we're not. We're in the middle of a
heat-wave.

Petey Are we? I'm so glad. If you will excuse me, I
must return to my work now.

Sophie Of course.

*Petey goes back to work, and we
hear the Food Dispenser grinding
and whirring. Then there is the
sound of a buzzer, and the **house
computer** speaks.*

Computer Good afternoon. I am pleased to announce that
you have a visitor.

Sophie A visitor? Who is it?

Computer He says his name is Sam.

Sophie Sam? That's not a visitor! That's my brother!

Computer Oh. Of course. I do apologize for my error. I
shall let Sam in straight away.

Sophie speaks to Petey.

Sophie   There's something definitely wrong with our house computer, Petey. That's the second mistake it's made.

Petey   You should ask your father to have it repaired.

Sophie   I will – if he ever turns off that stupid Ultra-Reality Machine.

Sam enters. He sounds fed up.

Sam	The computer wouldn't let me in!
Sophie	I know.
Sam	I kept telling it my name, but it didn't recognize my voice.
Sophie	There's some kind of loose connection. We'll have to get it looked at.
Sam	You can say that again.
Petey	Good afternoon, Sam. You are looking very cheerful.
Sophie	I don't think he is, Petey. Cheerful is the last thing he looks.
Sam	*(Miserably)* You're right. I'm fed up. *Really* fed up.
Sophie	How come?
Sam	It's Friday, isn't it? And we play jet-football on Fridays.
Sophie	Oh. I see. How did you get on?
Sam	The usual. We lost. Eight-nil. And they said it was my fault.

Sophie   It wasn't, though, was it?

Sam   It wasn't *all* my fault. It's my jet-pack. I just can't control it. If I want to go one way, it goes the other way! If I want to go up, it goes down! If I want to go down, it goes up! The other boys can control theirs, so why can't I?

Sophie   Maybe you just need some practice.

Sam   I know. Dad said he'd practise with me, but he never has. And I don't think he ever will.

Sophie   Well, it's all over now, Sam. We've got the whole weekend to look forward to.

Sam   *(Cheering up)* And dinner! I'm starving. What have we got to eat, Petey?

Petey whirrs and buzzes.

Sophie	We'll have to wait a bit while he finds the answer.
Sam	Not too long, I hope.
Sophie	Here it comes now.
Petey	Tonight for dinner we have roast beef, Yorkshire pudding, mashed potatoes, and carrots. I'll just put them in this cup for you.

We hear the sound of four pills being dropped into a cup.

There you are.

Sam   Thanks, Petey.

Petey   And here are yours, Sophie.

Sophie   Thanks.

> *Petey drops some pills into a cup
> for Sophie. She and Sam eat the
> pills one after the other.*

Sam   The food *sounds* good, but these pills always
               taste the same. They could be anything. I
               wonder what real food tasted like? You know,
               like they used to eat in the old days?

Sophie   I don't know. And I don't suppose we ever will.
               That reminds me, I've got a lot of history
               homework. I'd better go and get started on it.
               Thanks for the dinner, Petey.

Petey	You're very welcome, Sophie.

Sophie is about to go, when Sam calls her back.

Sam	Sophie –
Sophie	What?
Sam	Take a look at Petey.
Sophie	What about him?

Sam	Look at him... his face... He looks like he's... smiling!
Sophie	Smiling? Of course he's not smiling! How could he? He's just a robot. Robots can't smile.
Sam	I know that. But, just then, for a moment... I'm sure he smiled.

Sophie narrates.

Sophie	I look at Petey. There might just be something that looks like a smile...

Then I shake my head and go upstairs to start my homework.

And soon I've forgotten all about Petey, because I'm working on my vid-screen on a history project about what life was like nearly two hundred years ago, in the 1990s. They didn't have vid-screens then, or house computers, or robots.

Sophie	And I'm just trying to imagine what it was really like then, when Sam comes in.

We are in Sophie's room.

Sam	*(Breathless, excited)* Sophie –
Sophie	What is it, Sam? I'm busy –
Sam	It's Petey –
Sophie	He hasn't broken down, has he?
Sam	No... at least, I don't think so...
Sophie	What about him, then?
Sam	He's... well, there's something very odd about him.

Sophie	What do you mean?
Sam	He went into his cupboard to recharge himself... and I was just going up to my room, when I heard... noises...
Sophie	What kind of noises?
Sam	It's hard to say... I think you'd better come and listen for yourself...

Sophie narrates.

Sophie	So we go downstairs and listen outside Petey's cupboard – and Sam's right. There are some very strange noises coming from there.

We're outside the cupboard, and we can hear Petey inside.

Petey	(From inside the cupboard) A – A – A – A – A – A – A –
Sam	Hear that?
Sophie	Yes.
Petey	A – A – A – A –

Sophie	What's he doing in there?
Sam	I don't know.
Petey	A – A – A – CHOOO!
Sam	But I think we'd better find out!

Sophie	You're right! *(She speaks to the door computer)* Open the door, Computer!
Computer	Of course, Sophie.

> *We hear the sound of the door swishing open. **Petey's** voice is louder. When he speaks, he sounds less like a robot, more human.*

Petey	A – A – A –
Sophie	Petey!
Petey	*(Cheerfully)* Oh! Sophie! Sam! Good to see you!
Sophie	What did you say?
Petey	I said, it's good to see you.
Sophie	That's what I thought you said. But... it didn't sound like your voice. It sounded... like you really were happy...
Petey	That's because I am.
Sam	Look, Sophie! He's smiling! Just like he was earlier. Petey's smiling!
Sophie	But that's not possible... is it?

Petey	A – A – A – A – CHOO!
Sam	Petey! What's that noise you're making?
Petey	It's supposed to be a sneeze.
Sam	A sneeze?
Petey	I'm trying to sneeze.
Sam	What? Trying to sneeze? Why?

Petey   Because I want to. I want to sneeze and I want
              to – *(Petey suddenly makes a big burping noise)*

              Blaaaarrp! – I want to burp, like that. And
              cough, and sniff, and yawn and feel goose-
              bumps on my arms and –

Sophie   Okay, Petey, we get the picture. But why do you
              want to do all those things?

Petey   Because I want to be more... human.

Sophie   More human? But you can't be human. You're a
              robot.

Petey   I know –

Sophie	You were made in a factory. You were delivered to our house in a box –
Petey	Yes, I know that –
Sophie	So how can you be human?
Petey	*(Burping)* Blaaarrrpp! There! Did it again! A burp!
Sam	No, that's not quite right, Petey. If you want to burp, it has to sound more like this –
Sophie	All right, Sam! There's no need for you to join in.
Sam	But I only want to help –
Sophie	I think we can leave the burps out of this.
Sam	I'll show you how later, Petey.
Petey	Thank you, Sam. That's very kind of you.

Sophie	Listen, Petey. Just being able to sneeze and cough... and things like that... it won't make you more human, you know.
Petey	Oh, yes. I understand that. It's only the start. There are other ways. Such as the writing of poetry.
Sam	Poetry?
Petey	*(Proudly)* I have begun to write poetry.
Sam	Write poetry?
Petey	Yes. If you would both be kind enough to listen, here is my first poem.

> **Petey** *gives a machine-like cough,*
> *then speaks.*

There was a young robot named Neil
That liked to eat things made of steel
Dessert was tin foil
Which he washed down with oil
Then he said, 'What a fabulous meal!'

Well? What do you think?

Sophie	Er... not bad...
Sam	For a first try...
Petey	*(Delighted)* Thank you. I am quite pleased with it myself.
Sophie	Sam, have you got your electronic screwdriver on you?
Sam	Course I have. I carry it everywhere.
Sophie	Can I borrow it for a moment?
Sam	What for?
Sophie	I want to try and find out what's made Petey suddenly start acting like this.
Sam	Okay. Here it is.

> *He gives her the screwdriver.*
> ***Sophie*** *speaks to Petey.*

Sophie	Petey, do you mind if I open up your front panel and take a look inside?

Petey   Of course not, Sophie. Be my guest.

Sophie   Thanks. Here we go, then.

         She starts to unscrew the panel.
         ***Petey** makes a noise, a little like a*
         laugh.

         What's the matter?

Petey   Nothing. It just tickles.

Sophie	Oh. Sorry.
Petey	That's okay.

> *Sophie* *has taken off the front panel.*

Sophie	There. Hold the panel, will you, Sam?
Sam	Right.

> *Sophie* *gives the front panel to Sam.*

Sophie	Now I'll just take a look inside.

> *She looks inside Petey.*

Sam	What can you see?
Sophie	Nothing much. Just wires. They're all jumbled and knotted together... Wait a minute... I think there's something here in the middle... If I can just untangle them... *(She gives a cry)* Oh! It moved!
Sam	What did?

Sophie	I don't know! Something... It moved again... It's alive!
Sam	What's alive?
Sophie	A creature. Here! It's furry... and its nose is twitching... and it's got a tail!
Sam	Let me have a look.

Sam looks.

Sam	I think I know what that is. It's a mouse. We did about them at school.
Sophie	A mouse! Yes. I remember seeing a picture of one in the Virtual Zoo. But this is real! A real, living creature! I've never seen a real animal before.
Sam	I've heard stories that there are still a few around. They live in holes and things. But how did this one get in here?
Sophie	I don't know. It must have crawled in while Petey was recharging himself sometime.
Sam	And how does it eat?
Sophie	Maybe it comes out and gets stuff from the kitchen.
Sam	Imagine that. A real live mouse living inside Petey!
Sophie	And that must be the reason why Petey's behaving differently. It must have got his wires crossed somehow.

Sam   Push it back inside. I think it's scared.

Sophie   Okay. *(She puts the mouse back)* Give me the panel. I'll just put that back. *(She screws the panel back on)* There you are, Petey.

Petey   Thank you. Is everything all right?

Sophie   Er... Everything's fine, Petey. *(To Sam)* What are we going to do?

Sam   I suppose we ought to tell Mum and Dad.

Sophie	Are you kidding? They're still in there on that Ultra-Reality Machine. Even if they heard us they wouldn't listen to us.
Sam	You're right. Let's just keep it to ourselves. A secret, between the two of us.
Petey	The three of us, Sam. I can keep secrets too.
Sam	Sorry, Petey. I was forgetting. The three of us.

Sophie narrates.

Sophie	Next day we're up good and early. Usually, Petey spends the night in stand-by mode, recharging his batteries. But this time he's ready and waiting for us. And he's spent the whole night working hard. First, he shows us a painting he's made.

*We go to **Petey** talking to Sophie and Sam.*

Petey	Now. Tell me the truth. What do you think?
Sam	It's... er... very life-like –

Sophie	It looks like the inside of the cupboard –
Petey	Yes! That's just what it is!

Sophie narrates.

Sophie	Then he says he wants to try wearing some clothes, so we raid Dad's wardrobe for some old ones that don't fit him any more, and Petey stands there, admiring himself in front of the mirror.

*We go to **Petey** and the **children**.*

Petey	They suit me, don't you think?

Sophie   Yes. I suppose they do. They look very... elegant.

Petey   They do, don't they?

Sam   They are a bit big, though, Petey.

Petey   I don't mind that. I like a loose look.

Sophie narrates.

Sophie   And he tells us jokes –

We go to Petey and the children.

Petey   Why did the robot cross the road?

Sophie   I don't know. Why *did* the robot cross the road?

Petey   Because his On-Board Navigation Unit directed him to.

Petey gives a machine-like laugh.

Sam   I think we'll have to do a little more work on jokes.

Sophie narrates.

Sophie   And he keeps on asking us questions –

*We go to **Petey** and the **children**.*

Petey   Sam, what is the exact cubic capacity of your stomach?

Sam   Sorry, Petey. I don't know that.

Petey   Mm. I shall have to find that out. We humans are very inquisitive, you know.

Sophie narrates.

Sophie	And as the morning passes, I get to like him more and more. It's impossible not to like him. Especially when, around lunchtime, he winks one eye at us several times, and says –

*We go to **Petey** and the **children**.*

Petey	I've got an idea. I'm going to make you two some food – real food, I mean, like they used to eat in the old days.

Sam	That sounds great! What are you going to make us?

Petey	In my memory files I've found something called a 'Jam Sandwich'. I can fiddle with the Food Dispenser so that it turns the ingredients into real food instead of pills. I'll call you when it's ready.

Petey goes into the kitchen.

Sam	Real food, Sophie! Food that actually tastes like food! I used to think we'd got the worst robot in the street, but now I think we've got the best. And not only in the street! In the whole town!
Sophie	Yes. And just imagine what it would be like if all robots were like Petey. Just think how... friendly they'd all be. And much more fun –
Sam	That could never happen, though, Sophie. Petey's like he is because of an accident. Because that mouse did something to his circuits.
Sophie	But if somebody could find out exactly what the mouse did... and then copy it... and build it into the circuits at the factory... you'd have a race of human robots!
Sam	But that would mean telling somebody about Petey – and all they'd do is try to fix him –
	*Suddenly, **Mum** enters. When she speaks, her voice is vague and dreamy.*
Mum	Hello, darlings –
Sophie	Mum! I thought you were on the Ultra-Reality Machine –

Mum	I was. Space Wars. It's so exciting. But it does make you hungry.
Sam	We'll get you something to eat if you like –
Mum	I just went into the kitchen for a snack, and I noticed something very strange about Petey.

Sophie	Did you? Really?
Mum	Have you noticed anything strange about him?

Sophie and Sam speak together.

Sam **Sophie** }	No.

Mum	I think there's something wrong with him. He is old, after all. Do you know, I even heard him singing to himself! Can you imagine? A robot, singing! There's definitely something wrong with him. But don't worry, darlings. Everything's going to be all right.
Sam	Why?

Mum   I've called the factory on the vid-phone.
            They've sent out a Corrections Squad van to fix
            him. So, that's that. Now... I must get back to
            Space Wars. I'm right in the middle of saving
            the universe.

Mum goes.

Sam   You see? I was right! The Corrections Squad!
            They'll come and take him away and fix him!
            Make him just a machine again. We can't let
            them do that, Sophie. We've got to warn Petey.
            And we've got to think of a way of stopping
            them.

Sophie narrates.

Sophie   As soon as we tell Petey about the Corrections Squad, a look of terror comes on to his face.

We are in the kitchen.

Petey   The Corrections Squad! Coming here! How long have we got?

Sophie   The adverts say they answer every call within ten minutes!

Sam   That means there's a van racing towards us right now!

Petey	I don't want to be just a machine again! I like being what I am!
Sophie	We like you as you are, too, Petey.
Petey	But what can we do? We can't outrun a Corrections Squad jet-van.
Sam	Oh yes we can!
Petey	How?
Sam	Jet-packs. They'll outrun one of their vans. I've got mine, and there are two of Dad's old ones.
Sophie	Are you sure, Sam?
Sam	Course I am. They're much faster –
Sophie	I don't mean that. I mean – you said yesterday you can't control yours – and we'll be flying above the city – you know how crowded it gets – it might be dangerous –
Sam	Don't worry about me, Sophie. I'll manage. I've got to. This is a matter of life and death.

We hear the sound of a buzzer.

Sophie	That's the front door!

*The **house computer** speaks, in a flat voice.*

Computer   Good afternoon. There is a robot from the Corrections Squad at the door. Shall I let it in?

Petey   It's them!

Sam   Don't worry, Petey. I won't let them take you. We'll leave by the back door. Come on. We've got to go now!

Sophie narrates.

Sophie   So we grab the jet-packs, hurry out of the back door, and then –

*We go back to **Petey** and the **children**.*

Sophie   Ready, Sam?

Sam   Yes.

Sophie   Ready, Petey?

Petey   Ready.

Sophie   Okay. Switch your jet-packs on – and away we go!

We hear the sound of the three jet-packs whooshing Sophie, Sam, and Petey up into the sky. **Sophie** narrates the journey.

Sophie   Off we zoom into the skies. There's a lot of traffic about for a Saturday afternoon – old couples out for a ride in their old-fashioned jet-cars; big air-buses, packed with passengers; teenagers zipping around and looping the loop on flying skateboards. It's a tough job for the three of us to stay together and not get hit. And then we glance back and see something that makes our hearts jump.

*We go to **Petey**, **Sam** and **Sophie**, zooming through the sky. **Sam** calls out.*

Sam   Look! The Corrections Squad van. It's following us!

Petey	Oh, no! What are we going to do?
Sophie	Make for the city centre! We might be able to lose them there! Follow me!

They zoom away.

Bank left! Through these tower blocks! Right! Left again!

Sam	There's the city ahead, Petey! We're getting nearer. I think everything's going to be okay!

*Suddenly, the voice of a **robot traffic controller** calls out.*

Controller	Halt! Stop there!
Sam	Oh, no! It's traffic control!
Sophie	No good! We can't stop! Come on!

*They whizz past the **controller**, who cries out.*

Controller	Halt! You are breaking traffic laws! Return immediately! Halt! You are breaking traffic laws...

*The **controller's** voice fades into the distance as they fly on. **Sophie** calls back.*

Sophie	Sorry! We can't stop! It's an emergency!
Sam	Sophie! We're getting away. We're losing them!
Petey	Does that mean we're going to make it?
Sam	Yes, Petey. I think it does. As soon as we get above the city –
Sophie	Oh, no!

Sam   Sophie? What's wrong?

We can hear the sound of Sophie's jet-pack spluttering.

Sophie   My jet-pack. Can't you hear it? It's running out of fuel.

Sam	Are you sure?
Sophie	Yes. I'll have to go down. You two go on without me –
Petey	We can't leave you behind, Sophie.
Sophie	You've got to –

                                    *We hear, booming out, the voice of a giant, speaking **advertising sign**.*

Sign	Bored with your life? Be anyone! Go anywhere! Do anything! Buy an Ultra-Reality Machine today!
Sam	Wait a minute! That giant advertising sign! We can all hide behind that.

                                    *They fly off to the advertising sign as **Sophie** narrates.*

Sophie	The advertising sign hovers high above the city. We fly over and land behind it – and just in time. Right at that minute my jet-pack gives out.

58

We go back to the three hiding behind the sign.

Petey   Are you all right?

Sophie   Yes, thanks, Petey. Can you see the Corrections Squad, Sam?

Sam   Yes. They've slowed down.

Sophie   Let me see.

Sophie looks from behind the sign.

Sam	It looks like they can't decide which way to go.
Sophie	Please let them go away. Please!
Sam	They are! They are going away!
Petey	I'm saved!
Sophie	*(Sadly)* No, you're not, Petey. They're turning round. And they're heading right this way!
Petey	Oh, dear. And for a moment I thought – oh dear.
Sophie	I'm sorry, Petey.
Petey	Yes. So am I.
Sophie	Looks like there's nothing we can do now but wait.
Sam	Yes, there is! There's something I can do!
Sophie	What?
Sam	I'm going out there to them. I'll tell them I've seen you. I'll send them off in another direction.
Petey	On a wild robo-goose chase, you mean.

Sam	Yes. That's it.
Sophie	But it's dangerous out there, Sam. It's really busy round here.
Sam	I'll be all right.
Sophie	But I thought –
Sam	See you! Wish me luck!

Sam whizzes off towards the Corrections Squad van. Sophie narrates.

Sophie	And off he goes, zooming out into the busy air-traffic, dodging cars, weaving in and out of jet-boards. He's forgotten his fear and he's flying like an expert. And all because of Petey. All because he likes him, and wants to help him.
	*We go back to **Petey** and **Sophie** behind the sign.*
Petey	Look, Sophie. He's almost there. He's waving at them.
Sophie	They've seen him. They're moving towards him. It's going to be all right, Petey!
	***Petey** suddenly cries out in horror.*
Petey	Oh, no!
Sophie	Petey?
Petey	That air-bus! It's heading straight for Sam!
Sophie	It'll slow down –
Petey	No. It isn't slowing down. It hasn't seen him!
	***Sophie** calls out.*
Sophie	Sam! Look out! Behind you! Sam!

Petey   It's no good. He can't hear you.

Sophie   What are we going to do? It's heading straight
                 for him!

Petey   I know what to do! He showed me! My friend
                   Sam showed me! He went out there to save me.
                   Now it's my turn to save him!

                        *Sophie narrates as we hear Petey's
                        jet-pack whoosh him away.*

Sophie   And without a second thought, Petey flies out
                   towards Sam –

Petey   Sam!

Sam   *(Surprised, as Petey scoops him up)* Whooah!

Sophie   – Grabs him just in time, and lifts him out of
                   the path of the air-bus.

Up he goes, circling round and down with Sam
in his arms. Then he stops, and hovers in the air
– and I see Sam fling his arms round Petey and
hug him. And he's still hugging him when the
Corrections Squad van comes up, and it's all
over.

*We go to **Petey**, **Sophie** and **Sam**,
sitting in the Corrections Squad
van as it flies through the sky.*

Sam   I'm sorry, Petey. I tried my best.

Petey   That's all right, Sam. I know you did.

Sam   If it hadn't been for that stupid bus –

Petey   Don't worry about it, Sam. You didn't get hurt,
and that's the most important thing.

Sophie narrates.

Sophie   We sit together in the Corrections Squad van as
it speeds through the sky towards the robot
factory. We're all feeling pretty miserable. But
I'm determined not to give up.

We go to the van.

Sophie   Listen, robot. I think you ought to take us back
home.

*The **robot** speaks in a mechanical
voice.*

Robot   I'm sorry. We have to go straight back to the
factory.

Sophie	But our parents will be wondering where we are.
Robot	I'm sorry. We have to go straight back to the factory.
Sophie	It won't take long. Just five or ten minutes.
Robot	I have my orders. We have to go straight back to the factory.
Sophie	Please. Can't you bend the rules a little and just take us home first?
Robot	It is more than my job is worth. We have to go straight back to the factory.
Sophie	Is that all you can say?

Petey	Don't blame the robot, Sophie. It can't help it. It's only doing what it's been programmed to do.
Sophie	So were you until yesterday. You changed, so why can't it?
Sam	It hasn't got a mouse living inside it.
Sophie	I'm going to give it a try, anyway. *(She shouts angrily at the robot)* Now, listen to me! Me and my brother aren't robots! We're humans! You were only told to take a robot to the factory! You weren't told to take two humans! So you'd better take us back to our house right now! If you don't, there'll be big trouble!

> *There is silence. The **robot** says nothing. We hear the sound of its computer whirring and humming.*

Sam	Sophie. I think you might have done it!
Sophie	Ssh. Wait. It's processing the information.

> *The whirring and humming stop.*

Robot	Very well. I will take you two back to your home.

Sam   Yes! Brilliant, Sophie!

Sophie   That was the easy bit. Now comes the hard bit.
             Trying to persuade Mum and Dad not to have
             Petey fixed.

Sam   Trying to get them even to hear us, you mean.
             That's the really hard bit.

*We go to **Sophie's** narration.*

Sophie   It does take a while for Mum and Dad to
understand what we're talking about. After they
turn off the Ultra-Reality Machine they have a
dazed, glazed look in their eyes, like they don't
know what's going on. We have to tell them two
or three times what's happened. And then, at
last, it sinks in.

*We go to **Sophie**, **Sam**, **Petey**,
Mum and **Dad** at home.*

Dad	Are you trying to tell us that Petey is a... person?
Sophie	Yes.
Dad	But that's ridiculous. I mean, you've only got to look at it to see it's a robot.
Mum	And robots aren't people, darling.
Sophie	But he behaves like one –
Mum	Petey may act like a person, but it isn't really one – it's just a machine.
Dad	And it needs fixing –

Sam	'Him', not 'it'. Petey's a him, and he doesn't need fixing!
Mum	Of course it – he does, darling. He's – it's not acting like a robot should.
Sophie	I know. That's what we've been trying to tell you. All the things he's been doing – painting, writing poems, telling jokes –
Dad	Yes, but all those things don't really make Petey human, do they? Not even dressing in my old clothes –

Sophie bursts out in anger.

Sophie	Maybe you're right! Maybe they don't! But I know something that does! He went and saved Sam, even though he knew he'd be caught! Ask him – ask him why he did it!

| **Mum** | All right, darling. *(She speaks to Petey)* Petey. Why did you save Sam? |
| **Petey** | Sam was in danger. Sam is my friend. So I had to help him. |

Mum	Even though you knew you'd be caught?
Petey	Sam is my friend.
Sophie	You see? That's more than human! That's heroic!

Mum	*(To Dad)* I wonder... if they might have a point...
Sophie	Besides! How can you two talk about behaving like humans? You spend all your time plugged into that stupid machine! You look and act like machines most of the time. Petey's more human than either of you. He knows more about me and Sam than either of you. He spends more time with us!
Sam	Good one, Sophie!

*There is a silence. **Mum** and **Dad** both realize the truth that Sophie has told them.*

Mum	I think... they do have a point.
Dad	Yes. Maybe we've had enough of that machine for a while. I think I might unplug it.

***Dad** unplugs the machine.*

There. I was beginning to get a bit tired of it, anyway.

*The **Corrections Squad robot**, who has been waiting nearby, now speaks.*

Robot   Excuse me. Am I to take this robot of yours in for repair, or not?

Sophie   Mum?

Mum   No, thank you. We've changed our minds. I'm sorry for putting you to all this trouble.

Robot   No problem. It is all part of the service. But you will be billed for the call. Thank you. Goodbye.

Petey speaks to the robot.

Petey	Goodbye. And no hard feelings.
Robot	Pardon?
Petey	I know you were just doing your job. No hard feelings, friend.
Robot	Friend? What is this 'friend'? I do not... understand... It does not... compute...
Sophie	Never mind, robot. Perhaps it will one day.

> *The **Corrections Squad robot** goes.*

Poor thing. I think Petey almost blew its circuits.

Petey	Oh, I wouldn't want to do that. I was only trying to be friendly.
Sophie	I know you were, Petey.
Dad	A robot who wants to be friendly. I thought I'd never live to see it.
Mum	And, I have to admit, I actually quite like it.

Petey	Does this mean that you're both happy for me to stay as I am?
Mum	Yes – Petey. It looks like it does.
Petey	Thank you. Thank you both very much indeed. I am deeply grateful.
Dad	No, Petey. We're the ones who are grateful. You saved our son from being injured. And you've saved us from turning into complete idiots!
Mum	I can't believe I'm saying this to a robot, but – I don't know how we can thank you.
Petey	Actually, I know a way.
Dad	You do?
Petey	Yes. Why don't you take us all out and buy us a synthi-ice cream?
Sophie	That's a great idea, Petey!
Sam	Yes! He's full of them!

Mum   It seems as if he is. Well, then. Let's go and get those ice-creams.

Dad   Just before we do – you two said all this came about because of a mouse?

Sophie   That's right, yes. A mouse made its nest in Petey's control panel.

Dad   I'd like to see it, if you don't mind. I've never seen a real mouse before.

Sam   We'd better ask Petey if he minds us having a look. Do you, Petey?

Petey   I don't mind at all – but I'm afraid you won't find anything in there except wires.

Sophie   Why not? What's happened to the mouse?

Petey   While you were all talking, it... crawled out.

Sam   Oh. Where did it go?

Petey   I don't know. I didn't see.

Sam	Maybe it went into that other robot. And maybe it'll make its nest in his wires, and he'll turn human! And then it'll go into another, and another – !
Mum	Calm down, Sam. I don't think that's very likely.
Sophie	It would be good, though, wouldn't it, if all the robots were like Petey.
Dad	Do you know? I think you're right. It would.
Sophie	And maybe some day somebody will come along and find a way of doing just that. What do you think, Petey?
Petey	Yes, Sophie. I think somebody probably will.

Sophie narrates.

Sophie	And he looks straight at me – as if he knows something I don't – and grins – and winks.

THE END

Treetops Playscripts
Titles in the series include:

Stage 10
**The Masked Cleaning Ladies
of Om**
by John Coldwell;
adapted by David Calcutt
    single: 0 19 918780 0
    pack of 6: 0 19 918781 9

Stupid Trousers
by Susan Gates;
adapted by David Calcutt
    single: 0 19 918782 7
    pack of 6: 0 19 918783 5

Stage 11
Bertha's Secret Battle
by John Coldwell;
adapted by David Calcutt
    single: 0 19 918786 X
    pack of 6: 0 19 918787 8

Bertie Wiggins' Amazing Ears
by David Cox and Erica James;
adapted by David Calcutt
    single: 0 19 918784 3
    pack of 6: 0 19 918785 1

Stage 12
The Lie Detector
by Susan Gates;
adapted by David Calcutt
    single: 0 19 918788 6
    pack of 6: 0 19 918789 4

Blue Shoes
by Angela Bull;
adapted by David Calcutt
    single: 0 19 918790 8
    pack of 6: 0 19 918791 6

Stage 13
The Personality Potion
by Alan MacDonald;
adapted by David Calcutt
    single: 0 19 918792 4
    pack of 6: 0 19 918793 2

Spooky!
by Michaela Morgan;
adapted by David Calcutt
    single: 0 19 918794 0
    pack of 6: 0 19 918795 9

Stage 14
Petey
by Paul Shipton;
adapted by David Calcutt
    single: 0 19 918796 7
    pack of 6: 0 19 918797 5

Climbing in the Dark
adapted from his own novel
by Nick Warburton
    single: 0 19 918798 3
    pack of 6: 0 19 918799 1